M000013530

A FRIEND
SHOULD BE
DRASTIC,
GYMNASTIC,
BUT MOST OF ALL
ELASTIC

A FRIEND SHOULD BE
DRASTIC, GYMNASTIC,
BUT MOST OF ALL
ELASTIC

BILLY SPRAGUE

ILLUSTRATIONS BY DENNAS DAVIS

WOLGEMUTH & HYATT, PUBLISHERS, INC.
BRENTWOOD, TENNESSEE

Wolgemuth & Hyatt, Publishers, Inc.
1749 Mallory Lane, Suite 110
Brentwood, Tennessee 37027

to my dear
RosaLynn,
for her undeserved
love.

A
FRIEND
SHOULD BE
DRASTIC

HE SHOULD
GO OVER
THE EDGE
WHEN YOU'RE IN
A PINCH

STAND FIRM
WHEN YOU'RE WRONG
AND NOT
BUDGE AN INCH

AND
CARRY YOUR
BURDEN
WITH BARELY
A FLINCH

AND A
FRIEND SHOULD
BE
GYMNASTIC

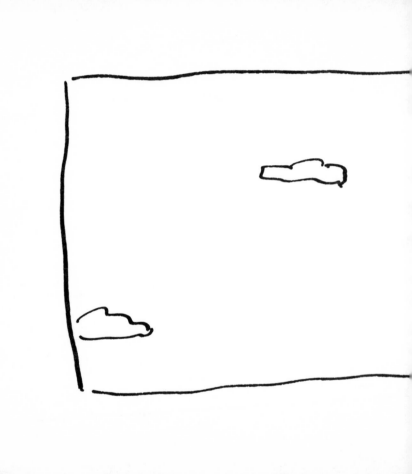

HE SHOULD
MUSCLE YOU UP
WHEN YOU
STUMBLE

BALANCE
THE FACTS
WHEN YOU
GRUMBLE

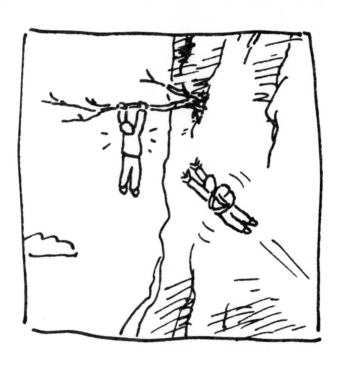

AND FLIP
INTO
PRAISE WHEN
YOU'RE
HUMBLE

BUT
MOST OF
ALL...

A FRIEND
SHOULD BE
ELASTIC

HE SHOULD
EXPAND YOUR
HORIZONS

STRETCH
YOUR
IMAGINATION

TIGHTEN
YOUR
MORALS

BUT LOOSEN
LIMITATIONS

HE SHOULD
SNAP BACK
TO YOUR SIDE
WHEN THE
WORLD TURNS
MEAN

AND
BEND OVER
BACKWARDS

TO
BELIEVE
IN YOUR
DREAMS